CATHOLICS

An Unauthorized, Unapproved, Illu

Rick Detorie

A Perigee Book

Perigee Books
are published by
The Putnam Publishing Group
200 Madison Avenue
New York, NY 10016

ISBN 0-399-51251-9

Printed in the United States of America
1 2 3 4 5 6 7 8 9 10

CATHOLICS

Introduction

Show me a Catholic who hasn't been slapped around, and I'll show you an Episcopalian.

The slaps came in many forms. A slap may have been an actual physical attack on a talkative fourth grader during assembly; or it could have been a figurative slap, an accusatory look directed at a second grader who spent his last nickel on candy instead of donating it to the mission drive. A slap could have taken the form of a warning to a first grader that his unkempt appearance would keep him out of a good college (not to mention the kingdom of heaven). A slap may also have been shrouded in the guise of constructive criticism, such as, "Why can't you be more like your older sister, an attractive, intelligent student, not at all like *you*?!"

These were typical slaps. They're also known as discipline, shame, embarrassment, guilt, torture, or penance. They were all part of our Catholic upbringing.

From day one of our formal Catholic education, we were taught by Sister how to be good Catholics. She taught us how to stand in a proper line (one arm's length from our neighbor); how to hold a pencil; how to shut up and listen; and how to memorize. And, boy, did we memorize. We committed to memory facts, dates, rules, dogma, and prayers. You couldn't be a good Catholic if you didn't have a good memory. Luckily, I have an excellent memory.

I remember Limbo, Venial Sins, Guilt, the Angelus, Holy Cards, When to Stand, the Sacred Heart, Guilt, My First Confession, the Rubber-Tipped Pointer, Retreat, When to Sit, Flying Chalk, the Martyrs, Dominus Vobiscum, Guilt, When to Kneel, the Stations of the Cross, Jug, Et Cum Spiri 220, and more.

Yes, I remember it all. In fact, I remember more, and with more accuracy, than Sister would have wanted me to.

So here it is: an illustrated record of a typical Catholic childhood.

Catholics will recognize most of it; non-Catholics will recognize the Catholics; but nobody will recognize everybody, because the names have been changed to protect the guilty.

Rick Detorie

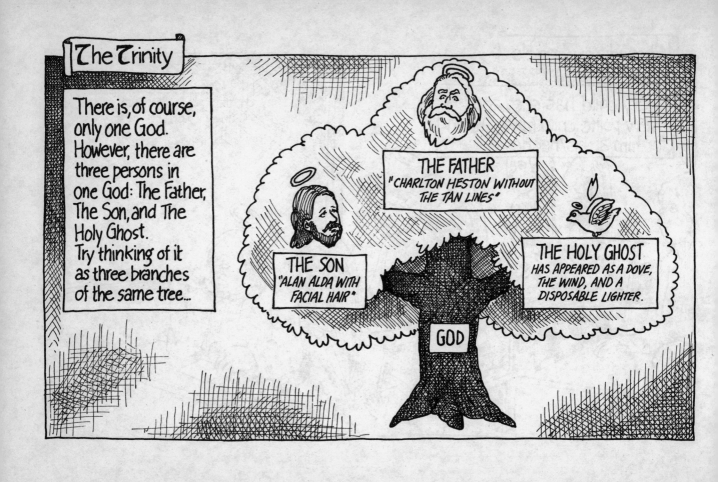

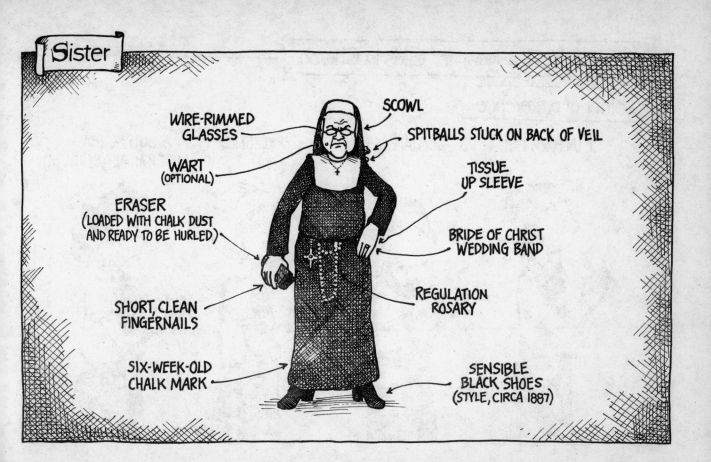

Sister

WIRE-RIMMED
GLASSES

SCOWL

SPITBALLS STUCK ON BACK OF VEIL

WART
(OPTIONAL)

TISSUE
UP SLEEVE

ERASER
(LOADED WITH CHALK DUST
AND READY TO BE HURLED)

BRIDE OF CHRIST
WEDDING BAND

SHORT, CLEAN
FINGERNAILS

REGULATION
ROSARY

SIX-WEEK-OLD
CHALK MARK

SENSIBLE
BLACK SHOES
(STYLE, CIRCA 1887)

The Three Faces of Sister Eve

Interesting Things to Look at During Mass

THE CLOTHING OF THE PERSON IN FRONT OF YOU

THE ALTAR BOY'S ILL-FITTING CASSOCK

STAINED GLASS WINDOWS

MOLES

DEAD LIGHTBULBS

STATUES

FAT PEOPLE TRYING TO GET OFF THEIR KNEES

STARING KIDS

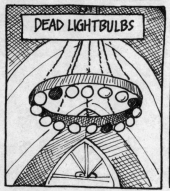

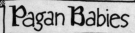

Pagan Babies

What public school kids bought with each five dollars they saved:

COMICS

MODEL EL 76

CANDY

What Catholic school kids bought with each five dollars they saved:

VERY GOOD, FRANCIS. AND WHAT WOULD YOU LIKE TO NAME YOUR PAGAN BABY*?

UH...JIM, PLEASE, SISTER.

CERTIFICATE
HOLY CROSS MISSIONARIES

*FOR FIVE DOLLARS YOU COULD "ADOPT" A PAGAN BABY (USUALLY AFRICAN OR ASIAN), I.E. A MISSIONARY WOULD BAPTIZE THE CHILD WITH THE NAME YOU SELECTED.

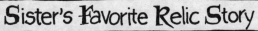

Sister's Favorite Relic Story

TWICE A YEAR, EVERY YEAR SINCE HIS DEATH IN 305 A.D. THE DRIED BLOOD OF ST. JANUARIUS, THE PATRON SAINT OF NAPLES, HAS TURNED TO LIQUID.

ONE DAY IN NAPLES:

AAAH!

LOOK, IT'S LIQUID!

OOOOO

IT'S A MIRACLE!

BIG DEAL! WHAT GOOD IS A DEAD GUY'S BLOOD?

SHUSH, GINO!

THE NEXT MORNING:

LOOK! MT. VESUVIUS IS ERUPTING!

THE LAVA IS HEADING THIS WAY!

WE'LL BE BURIED!

RUN FOR IT!!

EEEE!

AAA!

GINO RAN TO THE CHURCH

FATHER! CAN YOU DO SOMETHING?!

IDEA!

MMM... HAND ME THAT BLOOD, GINO!

FATHER RUSHED THE SACRED RELIC TO THE EDGE OF TOWN, WHERE, MIRACULOUSLY...

THE LAVA IS TURNING AWAY, SPARING NAPLES!

I WILL NEVER AGAIN DOUBT THE VALUE OF CATHOLIC MIRACLES!

AMEN!

GINO NEVER AGAIN DOUBTED THE CHURCH AND HE LIVED HAPPILY EVER AFTER AS A GOOD CATHOLIC.

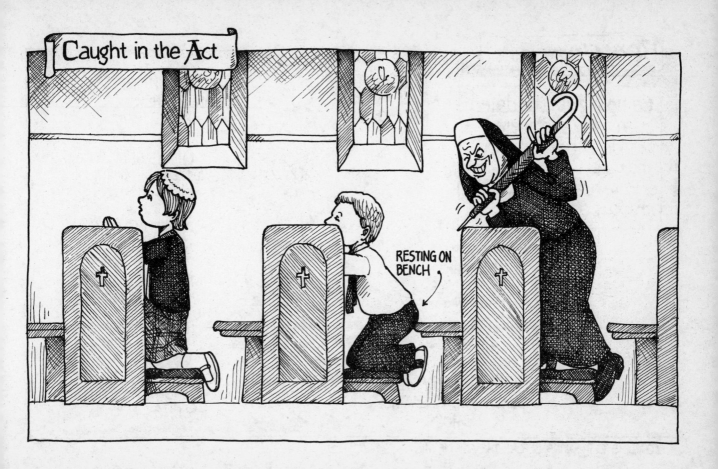

"Boy Crazy" Girls

Catholic girls who dated at an early age* were branded "boy crazy" by the nuns.

Here are the traits of the boy crazy girl:

WRITES BOYS' NAMES ON HER NOTEBOOK

LETS HER HAIR HANG IN HER FACE

CHEWS GUM (AND KEEPS IT HIDDEN IN HER CHEEK)

UNBUTTONS HER TOP BUTTON

ROLLS HER SKIRT FROM THE WAIST (TO SHORTEN IT)

TRIES TO GET AWAY WITH CLEAR NAIL POLISH

LETS HER SLIP SHOW

INTENTIONALLY WEARS BLACK PATENT LEATHER SHOES

WEARS HER SHOE STRAPS SLUNG BACK (VERY COOL!)

* ACCORDING TO THE NUNS, BEFORE THE AGE OF THIRTY.

How Catholics Know Spring Is Near

What four clues in this picture indicate the approach of spring?

1. **MEATLESS LUNCH**: AT THIS TIME OF THE YEAR, CATHOLICS ARE SUPPOSED TO EAT MEAT ONLY ONCE A DAY (USUALLY DINNER).
2. **PURPLE BAG ON SACRED STATUE**.
3. **ASHES**: ALTHOUGH IT HAS BEEN WEEKS SINCE ASH WEDNESDAY, BILLY, A SLOB, STILL HAS ASHES ON HIS FOREHEAD.
4. **GIVE-UPS**: THIS IS THE TIME OF YEAR WHEN GOOD CATHOLICS MAKE THE SACRIFICE OF GIVING UP SOMETHING THEY LIKE, LIKE PEANUT BUTTER. THAT'S RIGHT, IT'S LENT!!! AND EASTER (AND SPRING) ARE LESS THAN FORTY DAYS AWAY!!

Mortal Sin

A MORTAL SIN IS A GRIEVOUS OFFENSE AGAINST GOD. IF YOU DIE WITH ONE ON YOUR SOUL, IT'S STRAIGHT TO HELL FOR YOU.

SOME TYPICAL MORTAL SINS:

MURDER (OR WANTING TO COMMIT A MURDER)

WORSHIPPING A FALSE GOD

MISSING MASS ON SUNDAY (OR A HOLY DAY OF OBLIGATION)

LYING

RELAX, BABE. THE CHECK'S IN THE MAIL.

PREMARITAL SEX

YEAH, HONEST, DEBBIE. THE SECOND ECUMENICAL COUNCIL APPROVED HEAVY PETTING ON THE FIRST DATE!

WATCHING "DYNASTY"

KISS ME, YOU ELDERLY SLUT, YOU!

Venial Sin

A VENIAL SIN ISN'T AS BAD AS A MORTAL SIN. IT WON'T SEND YOU TO HELL, BUT IT WILL ADD TO YOUR PURGATORY TIME.

SOME TYPICAL VENIAL SINS:

WEARING DIRTY SOCKS TO MASS

CALLING YOUR SISTER A NAME

FORGETTING YOUR GRANDMOTHER'S BIRTHDAY

LYING

WEARING A ROSARY AROUND YOUR NECK

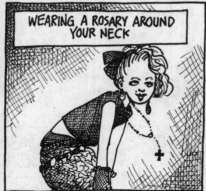

WEARING MAKEUP*

*A MORTAL SIN IF YOU'RE A BOY

WHICH OF THESE RELICS IS OLDER?

THE PRESERVED TOENAIL CLIPPING OF ST. PASCHAL WHO DIED IN 1592,

OR SISTER MARY XAVIER WHO HAS BEEN TEACHING FOR ABOUT AS LONG?

Sister's Favorite Mass Story

A CONGREGATION OF GOOD CATHOLICS WAS ATTENDING MASS...

WHEN SUDDENLY THE CHURCH WAS ATTACKED BY COMMUNISTS!

EEAAAH!

EEK!

AHHH!

EEEK!

RENOUNCESKI YOUR FAITHSKI!

SLAP

SLAP

SLAP

TO PROTECT THE CONSECRATED HOST, THE PRIEST PLACED IT IN THE MONSTRANCE...

AAAAH!

SLAP SLAP.

...AND, CARRYING THE MONSTRANCE, WALKED INTO A PILLAR.

SLAP SLAP SLAP

NO!

EEAAH!

SLAP

A MIRACLE!

PRAISE BE TO GOD!

LOOKSKI, COMRADES!

AAH!

LOOK!

DID YOU SEE THAT?

THE COMMUNISTS CONVERTED TO CATHOLICISM.

AND TO THIS DAY, THAT PILLAR, WITH THE PRIEST AND MONSTRANCE INTACT, RESIDES SOMEWHERE IN THE VATICAN.

Once a year, Catholic kids impersonated a giant singing rosary. The boys, dressed in dark suits, were the rosary links; and the girls, grouped according to the colors of their dresses, were the decades.

Everyone sang hymns as they paraded around the school grounds until, finally, a special young lady (pre-selected by Sister) placed a crown of posies upon the BVM's head to the tune of "O Mary, We Crown Thee with Blossoms Today."

BRING FLOWERS OF THE FAIREST. BRING FLOWERS OF THE RAREST...

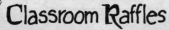

Classroom Raffles

NOT ONLY WERE THEY FOR A WORTHY CAUSE, BUT THEY TAUGHT US A VALUABLE LESSON AS WELL...

TODAY'S RAFFLE IS FOR ANOTHER VERY GOOD CAUSE. THE MONEY WILL GO TOWARD BUYING MUCH-NEEDED NEW RUBBER SHEETS FOR THE MOTHER HOUSE.

CHANCES COST A NICKLE APIECE, AND YOU MAY BUY AS MANY AS YOU LIKE.

GEE, I HAVE FIFTY CENTS. IT'S MY LUNCH MONEY, BUT GOLLY... IT **IS** FOR A **GOOD CAUSE!**

TEN CHANCES, PLEASE.

LATER
AND THE WINNER IS...

JOHN CUSTY!

I WON!

AND HERE'S YOUR PRIZE. IT'S A PICTURE OF THE MARTYR, ST. SEBASTIAN, PIERCED WITH ARROWS AND PASTED TO A PIECE OF CARDBOARD.

MUNCH
MUNCH
MUNCH MUNCH
MUNCH

THE VALUABLE LESSON: GAMBLING DOESN'T PAY.

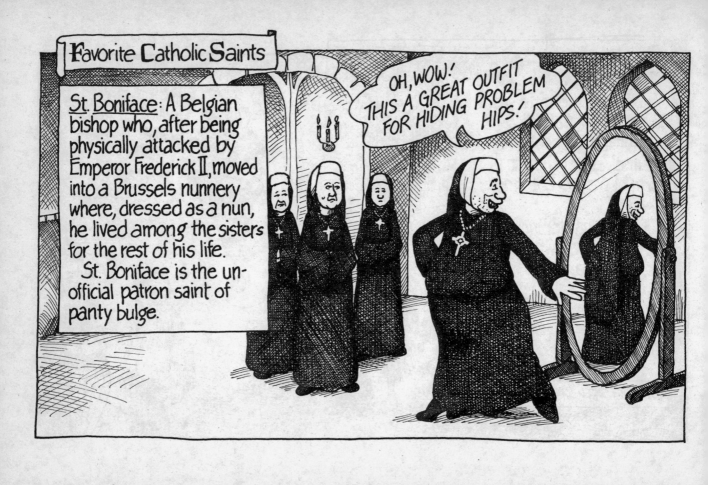

Brothers We Have Known
(LISTED BY NICKNAME)

"STINKY"

HISTORY

"MAD DOG"

ENGLISH

"POPS"

THEOLOGY

"LUGER"

CALCULUS, GERMAN

"MOOSE"

ALGEBRA, MATRICES

"PORKY"

LATIN, PHYSICS

"NERNY"

BIOLOGY, CHEMISTRY

"FRENCHY"

FRENCH, ART

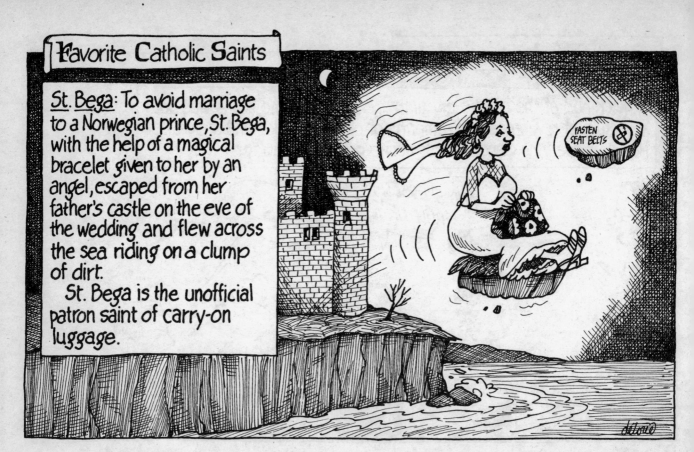

Favorite Catholic Saints

St. Bega: To avoid marriage to a Norwegian prince, St. Bega, with the help of a magical bracelet given to her by an angel, escaped from her father's castle on the eve of the wedding and flew across the sea riding on a clump of dirt.

St. Bega is the unofficial patron saint of carry-on luggage.